Core Knowledge Language Arts®

Fables

Unit 3 Reader

Skills Strand

GRADE 1

Amplify learning.

Core Knowledge®

Table of Contents
Fables
Unit 3 Reader

Pausing Point (Stories for Assessment and Extra Practice)

King Log and King Crane

Once the frogs said, "We wish we had a king! We need a king! We must have a king!"

The frogs spoke to the gods. They said, "We ask you, the gods, to send us a king!"

"The frogs <u>are</u> f**oo**ls," s<u>ai</u>d the gods. "As a joke, let us send them a big log to b<u>e</u> th<u>ei</u>r king."

The gods got a big log and let it drop. The log fell in the pond and made a big splash.

The frogs w<u>ere</u> scared of the log. Th<u>ey</u> s<u>ai</u>d, "King Log is strong! W<u>e</u> must hide fr<u>o</u>m him in the grass!"

As time went by, the frogs came to see that King Log was tame. He did not bite. He did not run. He just sat there.

"King Log is not a strong king!" said one frog.

"I wish we had a strong king!"

"I do, too!"

"We must have a strong king!"

The frogs spoke to the gods. They said, "We ask you, the gods, to send us a strong king, and send him soon!"

This time the gods sent a crane to be king of Frog Land.

King Crane was not like King Log. He did not just sit there. He ran fast on his long legs, and he ate lots of the frogs.

The frogs were sad.

"King Crane is a bad king," they said. "We miss King Log! He was a fine king. We made a bad trade!"

The frogs spoke to the gods. They said, "We ask you, the gods, to send us back King Log!"

The gods were mad. "Fools!" they said. "You said you must have a strong king. We sent you one. He is yours to keep!"

11

The Two Dogs

Once two dogs met. One of them was a tame dog who made his home with men. One was a dog who ran free.

The dog who ran free stared at the tame dog and said, "Why is it that you are so plump and I am so thin?"

"Well," said the tame dog, "I am plump because the men feed me. I do not have to run all the time to get my food. My job is to keep the home safe when the men are in their beds. When they wake up, they feed me scraps of food from their plates."

"Your life must be a fine life," said the thin dog. "I wish my life were like yours."

The plump dog said, "If you will help me keep the home safe, I bet the men will feed you, too."

"I will do it!" said the thin dog.

But just as the thin dog said this, the m**oo**n shone on the neck of the plump dog.

The thin dog said, "What is that on y<u>ou</u>r neck?"

"I am on a rope <u>wh</u>en the sun is up," said the plump dog.

"Rope?" said the thin dog. "D<u>o</u> they keep you on a rope?"

"Yes," said the plump dog. "When the moon is up, the men let me run free, but when the sun shines, they keep me on a rope. I can not run and be free when the sun is up, but it is not so bad."

"No, no!" said the thin dog, as he ran off. "I will not have a rope on my neck. You can be plump. I will be free!"

The Hares and the Frogs

Three hares stood in the grass.

"I am sad," one of them said. "I wish we were brave."

"So do I," said the next one. "But we are not brave. A splash in the brook scares us. The wind in the grass scares us. We are scared all the time."

"Yes," said the last one. "It is sad to be a hare."

Just then there was a splash in the br**oo**k. The splash scared the hares. They ran off to hide. As they ran, they scared a bunch of frogs.

"L**oo**k," said one of the hares. "The frogs <u>are</u> scared of us!"

"Yes, they <u>are</u>!" said the next hare. "They <u>are</u> scared of us! Well, I'm glad I am not a frog!"

"Yes!" said the last hare. "In the end, it is g**oo**d to b<u>e</u> a hare!"

The Two Mules

Once a man went on a trip with two mules. He set five packs on one mule and five packs on the next one.

The black mule was strong. The mule with spots was not as strong, and by noon, he was tired. The mule with the spots felt the packs press on his back and he could not keep up with the black mule.

The mule with the spots spoke to the black mule. "I hate to ask," he said, "but would you help me with my packs?"

The black mule did not stop to help the mule with spots.

"I have my five packs and you have your five," he said.

The mule with spots went on as long as he c<u>ou</u>ld. At last, he fell and c<u>ou</u>ld not get up.

The man set all ten of the packs on the black mule.

"What a f**oo**l I was!" the black mule said. "I did not help the mule with spots <u>when</u> I sh<u>ou</u>ld h<u>a</u>v<u>e</u>. If I had, I w<u>ou</u>ld not h<u>a</u>v<u>e</u> to lift all of his packs as well as mine."

The Dog and the Mule

Once there was a man who had a dog and a mule. The man gave the dog scraps of food from his plate. He let the dog lick his spoon. The dog would sit on the man's lap and lick him. The man would rub the dog and kiss him.

The mule would look in and see the dog on the man's lap. He felt sad. He felt left out.

"The man feeds me," said the mule, "but I do not get food from his plate. I'm left out because I am a mule. I should act like a dog. If I do that, the man will like me just as much as he likes the dog."

So the mule left his pen and went in the man's home. He set his feet on the man's lap and gave the man a big, wet lick.

The man was scared. He gave a sh**ou**t and let his plate drop. It broke with a crash. The man fell down, t**oo**.

When the man got up, he was mad at the mule. He made the mule run back **ou**t to his pen.

The Bag of Coins

Once two men went on a trip. One of them found a bag of coins on the ground, at the foot of a tree.

"Look what I found!" he said. "It is a bag of coins!"

"Good!" said the next man. "We can count the coins and see what we have!"

"No," said the man with the bag. "The coins in this bag are not our coins. They are my coins. I found them. They are all mine!"

Just then there was a **lou**d
sh**ou**t. There w<u>ere</u> a bunch of
men and they w<u>ere</u> mad.

"L**oo**k!" they sh**ou**ted. "There
is a man with the bag. He stole
our c**oi**ns!"

"Get him!" said the rest.

The man with the **coi**ns was
scared. "Those men are mad,"
he said. "If they see us with the
coins, we will b<u>e</u> in a bad spot."

"N<u>o</u>, n<u>o</u>," said the man next
to him. "If they see *you, you* will
b<u>e</u> in a bad spot. Those are
not ***ou**r* **coi**ns. Those are <u>*your*</u>
coins. *You* f**ou**nd them. They
are all <u>*yours*</u>."

The Dog and the Ox

Once a dog took a nap on a pile of straw in a box. But the straw in the box was not a bed.

When the ox came home, he saw the straw in his food box. But he could not get to the straw because the dog was on top of it.

49

"Dog," said the ox, "could you sleep up in the loft? I would like to munch on the straw in my food box."

The dog woke up, but he would not get off the straw. He was mad that the ox woke him up.

At last, a man came in and saw the dog on the straw.

"Bad dog!" said the man. "You did not need that straw, but you would not let the ox have it! Shame on you! Get up!"

The Fox and the Grapes

A fox s**aw** a bunch of ripe grapes that hung fr_o_m the branch of a tree.

The fox said, "Those grapes **loo**k g**oo**d. I will get them and make them m_y_ lunch."

The fox st**oo**d up on his back legs, but he c_ou_ld not grab the grapes.

The fox made a hop, but he could not grab the grapes.

The fox ran and made a big jump, but he still could not get the grapes.

At last, the fox sat down on the ground.

"What a fool I am!" said the fox. "I can tell that those grapes are sour. They would not have made a good lunch."

The Fox and the Hen

A hen sat in a tree. A red fox ran up to the tree.

"Did they tell you?" said the fox.

"Tell me what?" said the hen.

"They h<u>a</u>v<u>e</u> made a **law**," said the fox. The **law** says that we must all be pals. Dogs are not to chase cats. They must be pals. Cats are not to chase rats. They must be pals. Dog and cat, fox and hen, snake and rat must all be pals! S<u>o</u> jump d<u>ow</u>n h<u>ere</u> and let m<u>e</u> hug you!"

"Well, that s**ou**nds swell!" said the hen. "But, all the same, I will sit up h<u>ere</u> a bit."

Then the hen said, "What's that I see?"

"<u>Where</u>?" said the fox. "What is it?"

"It l**oo**ks like a pack of dogs," said the hen.

"Dogs!" said the fox. "Then I must get **ou**t of h<u>ere</u>!"

"Stop!" said the hen. "The **law** says that dog and fox must be pals. S<u>o</u> you are safe!"

But the fox did not stop. He ran off.

The hen just smiled.

The Fox and the Crane

The fox **saw** the crane and said, "Crane, will you have lunch with m<u>e</u>?"

The crane said, "I will."

The crane came and sat d<u>ow</u>n with the fox in his den.

The fox was up to a trick. He gave the crane s<u>o</u>m<u>e</u> f**oo**d, but he gave it to him in a flat stone dish. The crane c<u>ou</u>ld not get the f**oo**d b<u>e</u>c<u>au</u>se of the shape of his bill. The fox smiled at his trick. He ate up all of his f**oo**d.

The next week the crane s**aw** the fox and said, "Fox, will you have lunch with m<u>e</u>?"

The fox said, "That w<u>ou</u>ld be g**oo**d. I will."

This time the crane was up to a trick. He gave the fox milk, but he gave it to him in a glass with a long, thin neck. The fox c<u>ou</u>ld not get the milk b<u>e</u>c<u>au</u>se of the shape of his nose.

The Tree and the Reeds

A pr**ou**d tree st**oo**d next to a grove of reeds. When a gust of wind came, the reeds bent in the wind. But the pr**ou**d tree did not bend at all. It st**oo**d up to the wind.

"It is **too** bad that you can't stand up to the wind as I can!" said the tree to the reeds.

"We bend s<u>o</u> that we will not crack," said the reeds.

"There is no wind that can crack m<u>e</u>!" said the tree in its pride.

"We shall see!" said the reeds.

The next week a big wind came. The tree was brave. It st**oo**d up a long time. But the gusts of wind w<u>ere</u> **too** strong. At last, there was a **lou**d crack. The tree fell with a crash.

The reeds bent in the strong wind, but they did not crack. They still stand b<u>y</u> the br**oo**k. You can see them wave in the wind next to the r**oo**ts of the tree.

The Moon

The m**oo**n said, "I wish I had a dress. Mom, will you make me a dress?"

The m**oo**n's mom said, "I will not make you a dress, my sweet."

"<u>Why</u> not?" said the m**oo**n.

"B<u>ecause</u> you wax and you wane," said the m**oo**n's mom. "One week you are big and r**ou**nd. The next week you are thin. One week you are all there. The next week there is just a bit of you. No one can make a dress that will fit you in all of <u>your</u> shapes!"

About this Book

This book has been created for use by students learning to read with the Core Knowledge Reading Program. Readability levels are suitable for early readers. The book has also been carefully leveled in terms of its "code load," or the number of spellings used in the stories.

The English writing system is complex. It uses more than 200 spellings to stand for 40-odd sounds. Many sounds can be spelled several different ways, and many spellings can be pronounced several different ways. This book has been designed to make early reading experiences simpler and more productive by using a subset of the available spellings. It uses *only* spellings that students have been taught to sound out as part of their phonics lessons, plus a handful of Tricky Words, which have also been deliberately introduced in the lessons. This means that the stories will be 100% decodable if they are assigned at the proper time.

As the students move through the program, they learn new spellings and the "code load" in the decodable Readers increases gradually. The code load graphic on this page indicates the number of spellings students are expected to know in order to read the first story of the book and the number of spellings students are expected to know in order to read the final stories in the book. The columns on the inside back cover list the specific spellings and Tricky Words students are expected to recognize at the beginning of this Reader. The bullets at the bottom of the inside back cover identify spellings, Tricky Words, and other topics that are introduced gradually in the unit this Reader accompanies.

Visit us on the web at www.coreknowledge.org

Core Knowledge Language Arts

Series Editor-in-Chief
E. D. Hirsch, Jr.

President
Linda Bevilacqua

Editorial Staff

Carolyn Gosse, Senior Editor - Preschool
Khara Turnbull, Materials Development Manager
Michelle L. Warner, Senior Editor - Listening & Learning

Mick Anderson
Robin Blackshire
Maggie Buchanan
Paula Coyner
Sue Fulton
Sara Hunt
Erin Kist
Robin Luecke
Rosie McCormick
Cynthia Peng
Liz Pettit
Ellen Sadler
Deborah Samley
Diane Auger Smith
Sarah Zelinke

Design and Graphics Staff

Scott Ritchie, Creative Director

Kim Berrall
Michael Donegan
Liza Greene
Matt Leech
Bridget Moriarty
Lauren Pack

Consulting Project Management Services

ScribeConcepts.com

Additional Consulting Services

Ang Blanchette
Dorrit Green
Carolyn Pinkerton

Acknowledgments

These materials are the result of the work, advice, and encouragement of numerous individuals over many years. Some of those singled out here already know the depth of our gratitude; others may be surprised to find themselves thanked publicly for help they gave quietly and generously for the sake of the enterprise alone. To helpers named and unnamed we are deeply grateful.

Contributors to Earlier Versions of these Materials

Susan B. Albaugh, Kazuko Ashizawa, Nancy Braier, Kathryn M. Cummings, Michelle De Groot, Diana Espinal, Mary E. Forbes, Michael L. Ford, Ted Hirsch, Danielle Knecht, James K. Lee, Diane Henry Leipzig, Martha G. Mack, Liana Mahoney, Isabel McLean, Steve Morrison, Juliane K. Munson, Elizabeth B. Rasmussen, Laura Tortorelli, Rachael L. Shaw, Sivan B. Sherman, Miriam E. Vidaver, Catherine S. Whittington, Jeannette A. Williams

We would like to extend special recognition to Program Directors Matthew Davis and Souzanne Wright who were instrumental to the early development of this program.

Schools

We are truly grateful to the teachers, students, and administrators of the following schools for their willingness to field test these materials and for their invaluable advice: Capitol View Elementary, Challenge Foundation Academy (IN), Community Academy Public Charter School, Lake Lure Classical Academy, Lepanto Elementary School, New Holland Core Knowledge Academy, Paramount School of Excellence, Pioneer Challenge Foundation Academy, New York City PS 26R (The Carteret School), PS 30X (Wilton School), PS 50X (Clara Barton School), PS 96Q, PS 102X (Joseph O. Loretan), PS 104Q (The Bays Water), PS 214K (Michael Friedsam), PS 223Q (Lyndon B. Johnson School), PS 308K (Clara Cardwell), PS 333Q (Goldie Maple Academy), Sequoyah Elementary School, South Shore Charter Public School, Spartanburg Charter School, Steed Elementary School, Thomas Jefferson Classical Academy, Three Oaks Elementary, West Manor Elementary.

And a special thanks to the CKLA Pilot Coordinators Anita Henderson, Yasmin Lugo-Hernandez, and Susan Smith, whose suggestions and day-to-day support to teachers using these materials in their classrooms was critical.

CREDITS

Every effort has been taken to trace and acknowledge copyrights. The editors tender their apologies for any accidental infringement where copyright has proved untraceable. They would be pleased to insert the appropriate acknowledgment in any subsequent edition of this publication. Trademarks and trade names are shown in this publication for illustrative purposes only and are the property of their respective owners. The references to trademarks and trade names given herein do not affect their validity.

All photographs are used under license from Shutterstock, Inc. unless otherwise noted.

WRITER
Matthew M. Davis

ILLUSTRATORS AND IMAGE SOURCES
Cover: Rebecca Miller; Title Page: Rebecca Miller; 1: Rebecca Miller; 3: Rebecca Miller; 5: Rebecca Miller; 7: Rebecca Miller; 9: Rebecca Miller; 11: Rebecca Miller; 13: Rebecca Miller; 15: Rebecca Miller; 17: Rebecca Miller; 19: Rebecca Miller; 21: Rebecca Miller; 23: Rebecca Miller; 25: Rebecca Miller; 27: Rebecca Miller; 29: Rebecca Miller; 31: Rebecca Miller; 33: Rebecca Miller; 35: Rebecca Miller; 37: Rebecca Miller; 39: Rebecca Miller; 41: Rebecca Miller; 43: Rebecca Miller; 45: Rebecca Miller; 47: Rebecca Miller; 49: Kathryn M. Cummings; 51: Kathryn M. Cummings; 53: Kathryn M. Cummings; 55: Rebecca Miller; 57: Rebecca Miller; 59: Rebecca Miller; 61: Rebecca Miller; 63: Rebecca Miller; 65: Rebecca Miller; 67: Rebecca Miller; 69: Rebecca Miller; 71: Rebecca Miller; 73: Rebecca Miller; 75: Rebecca Miller; 77: Kathryn M. Cummings; 79: Kathryn M. Cummings